Single-Handed

Single-Handed

General practitioners in remote and rural areas

Rosie Donovan and John Bain

Whittles Publishing

Typeset by
Whittles Publishing Services

Published by
Whittles Publishing,
Roseleigh House,
Latheronwheel,
Caithness, KW5 6DW,
Scotland, UK

ISBN 1-870325-09-5

Printed by J.W.Arrowsmith Ltd., Bristol

Contents

vii Foreword

ix General practitioners in remote and rural areas

xi Reflections on events in practice

xvii The authors

1 The Northern Islands – Orkney and Shetland

21 The North – Lybster, Bonar Bridge, Lairg, Cromarty, Helmsdale and Canisbay

35 The North-East – Edzell, Tomintoul, Strathdon, Tarland, Torphins and Buckie

49 The North and West Highlands – Torridon, Lochcarron and Durness

57 The Western Highlands – Lochaline, Port Appin, Arisaig, Salen, Laggan and Kinlochleven

71 The Western Isles – Skye, Lewis, Harris and Tiree

89 The South-West Highlands – Muasdale, Southend, Tarbert, Tighnabruaich, Isle of Arran, Isle of Islay and Drummore

105 The South – Ecclefechan and Lauder

111 Acknowledgements

Foreword

As we move into a new century, this is an extremely apposite 'snapshot' of a significant number of single-handed general practitioners working in the more remote areas of Scotland. At a time of constant change in the National Health Service in Scotland, it will compel the reader to contemplate what we as health professionals, and crucially, as patients, really value as key elements of traditional general practice. The current shift towards larger practices, particularly in urban and even rural areas, is in sharp contrast to the personal services offered by this group of devoted doctors.

The personality of each practitioner shines through in the immensely illuminating black and white portraits. The short account from each one highlights the professional isolation which these individuals endure, but it is heartening that all express the positive attributes of single-handed practice with enthusiasm. The sense of duty to their patient communities is clearly evident. Battling against the elements, making a sea crossing or struggling a mile along a muddy footpath in pitch darkness add an element to a simple house visit which many of us would never have to consider. The need to summon a helicopter, air ambulance or lifeboat adds additional stress to the decision to admit a patient to hospital.

As a humble 'townie' GP, who practises only six miles from a large hospital, one can only admire the skill and commitment of these colleagues, many of whom I have had the pleasure and privilege of meeting during my chairmanship.

Colin Hunter OBE FRCGP
Chairman Scottish Council
Royal College of General Practitioners

General practitioners in remote and rural areas

King James V is credited with being Scotland's first physician, and he often spent time at Castle Stalker in Appin, which was extended in 1540 for the King by Alan Stewart, third clan chief. Thus single-handed rural practice began in Scotland! Over the next four centuries, medicine was organised in haphazard ways in rural Scotland; by clans in the Highlands until the battle of Culloden, after which the churches became the main source of social organisations. Some parishes provided inducements such as a house or several carts of peat or amounts of food to attract doctors to an area. Each doctor or nurse was the unit of medical care.

The Statistical Account of 1848 highlights the gross variation in medical attention in the rural areas and the huge variation in standards between incredibly dedicated philanthropic characters, ceaselessly committed to large parts of the poor rural areas, to slothful drunks who were of limited assistance even if present and sober. At Fasnacloich, the Wishing Well was reported to be more popular than Dr Livingstone, the hapless local doctor. Following the 1848 Statistical

Account, many parishes adopted "best practice" ideas and a gradual improvement of medical provision occurred.

By 1905, the government became involved directly in medical provision in the Highlands & Islands, when the Dewar Commission into Medical Attendance in the Highlands & Islands was set up. This Commission produced a landmark report upon which medical provision in this region throughout the twentieth century and ultimately the National Health Service was established. It visited many remote areas of the Highlands & Islands and took evidence from ordinary people and made very far-reaching recommendations about the threshold for medical attendance, especially Queen's Nurses who should be present on a list of islands and remote areas unless their population dropped below 100 inhabitants – remarkably low levels by today's standards. It is arguable that Dewar did more for health care in the Highlands than anybody in history and if you consider that infant mortality in 1905 was 125 deaths per 1000 births, and was 5 per 1000 births at the end of the century, statistics support the argument.

Having demanded better medical attendance, the population of the Highlands & Islands dug deep into their pockets and raised substantial parts of the Queen's Nurses' salaries. The Government was persuaded to contribute to the doctors' inducement as the Highlands & Islands Medical Service was established and Lloyd George's Medical Panels were set up in 1911. Individual doctors ran their practices as they saw fit, with nurses covering designated areas. Many doctors gave a lifetime's service to their practices, with very little support from the authorities and very little time off – notes on the surgery door such as "Gone to the glen" or "Gone fishing" were common, but always expecting a casualty upon their return.

In 1933 the first air ambulance flight was to a single-handed practice – North Uist – where the terminally ill minister was flown home from Glasgow Western Infirmary to die at home in the Hebrides; a telling statement as to the values of single-handed practice, that bringing a person home for terminal care was worthy of the first air ambulance, in contrast to today's values of flying into the centre of excellence for 'high tech' treatment.

In 1948 the National Health Service took over the running of the service for doctors and nurses and it is still a source of resentment in the small islands that, having taken over the cost of the Queen's Nurses, the NHS tried to reduce the service provided. In the 1950s and 1960s practice continued much as before the Health Service although the playing field was more level. In 1973 the Inducement Practitioners' Association was formed in Fort William, an organisation that has grown to represent the 120 practitioners who receive an inducement in Scotland – practitioners from Drummore in Galloway to Unst in Shetland. More recently the newly established Remote and Rural Resource Initiative could well encourage a brave new world of single-handed rural practice.

This book focuses on single-handed doctors, a unique band who serve small and isolated communities throughout both the Highlands and Islands and other remote areas in Scotland. The area of Scotland loosely referred to as the Highlands covers around a third of the country and for the most part has a rugged terrain with a sparse population. For people living in remote rural areas access to a general practitioner is critical to their sense of community. This concept of community is vital to the well-being of people living in these areas and the local doctor is a vital part of the scene. Practice in a rural area is unique in that the doctors are not just working in the community, but are very much part of that community. To work in a rural community means that private and working lives are inextricably linked. If there is anything true of small rural medical practices it is that no two are alike.

Doctors who choose to be single-handed are self selected, each one of them finding the places and jobs that suit their personalities and they are moulded by the situation in which they find themselves. Boundaries between doctor, patient, friend and acquaintance are always blurred in these small practices. Patients are well informed about the details of the doctor's life, recreation, family and a host of personal matters. For his (or her) part, the doctor often knows more about the patient than the formal medical notes would indicate. This visibility can be difficult to manage and those coming from an urban environment may take some time to adapt and to discuss the social skills in a remote sparsely populated rural environment. However, it is being part of the community that makes single-handed practice a unique experience.

There are, of course, difficulties in being a single-handed doctor. The isolation, the lack of time off, the problem of taking important decisions with no immediate backup. Despite these, the general practitioners love their work, their patients and their way of life and most of them wouldn't change their circumstances. The compensations include living in some of the most beautiful parts of Scotland, and the opportunity to be totally independent without interference from partners. Some are mountain climbers, but the irony is that having arrived in the mountains there is often little opportunity to climb them because the doctors are on call 24 hours a day.

At a time when recruitment to single-handed practice causes concern, there is a need to explore and record the lives of doctors in these practices. While the creation of the associate practitioner scheme which provides part-time help for rural doctors has alleviated the pressures of isolation, the ultimate responsibility for patient care still lies in the hands of those who have chosen to pursue their professional lives "far from the madding crowd". The advent of telemedicine which provides video links between remote doctors and specialist units may lead to improvements in care, but could also lead to policies which result in a reduction in the number of doctors in far flung areas. The move towards co-operatives to cover for night call may also lead to similar arrangements for daytime working with the end result being that one doctor and a number of associates may cover a much wider geographical area than currently. This means that single-handed practice may be under threat and it is an opportune time to review how these doctors see their roles and future prospects.

The stimulus for this book came from a chance meeting between the two authors, when Rosie Donovan was showing her exhibition "Ex

Patria" which recorded the lives of a selection of Scots now resident in Canada. When speaking about future projects, John Bain suggested that single-handed doctors in remote areas could form the basis of an interesting and important record of their lives, and from that idea grew the following depiction of single-handed general practitioners in rural Scotland. The book is based on a series of taped consultations with GPs working in isolated communities who also agreed to be identified in person and by photographic record. In the chapters which follow, 47 of around 200 single-handed doctors in Scotland report on their experiences and provide an insight to their unique contributions to health care in Scotland.

Reflections on events in practice

Memories

A winter's afternoon; the day for the weekly visit to the distant village in the practice.

I had taken the blood tests and given the injection he so hated — part of his long battle against the advancing disease. It took time for him to psyche himself up for the venepuncture, so we'd have a chat and a cup of tea. It wasn't an occasion for hurrying.

As I gathered up my things, I could see that snow was falling. He carried my bag down the steep stairs to the front door, as he always did. "You take care and watch that road" he said as I set off on the 20 miles home to the evening surgery.

Two and a half years later, I stood with his family in that same room as his long struggle with illness came gently to an end. I thought about his courage through difficult symptoms and difficult treatment, about his perky spirit, about his love for his family. It brought many personal thoughts too; for it was only nine months since my own husband had died. They were alike in some ways, those two men; same age group, both belonging to a great Scottish city, both facing dreadful illnesses with courage, spirit and determination.

I moved to the window, away from the family group beside the still figure in the bed, and I felt the tears pricking my eyes.

Night call

I had just gone to bed about midnight, when the phone rang. A young, unrecognised, rather hesitant male voice asked if I would come and see his mother who was unwell in a holiday cottage right on the periphery of the practice area. I knew where these cottages were but had never been there – you reached the house at the end of the tarred road, 20 miles from my home and then walked about one mile along the track to these isolated cottages which had no piped water or electricity, but where a community had once lived. A beautiful place, but not in the middle of the night!

The lady's symptoms sounded potentially serious so 45 minutes later I reached the end of the tarred road where my escort was waiting. His torch was working, which was more than could be said for mine! We climbed up the track into the darkness. As we progressed over the soggy path, I began to wonder how I was going to get this lady out of here, if she needed to be admitted to hospital. Our Health Board helicopter didn't fly at night, and even if I could arrange a rescue flight, I had no knowledge of any suitable landing site on this exposed promontory. Would we, with my ambulance colleagues, have to carry this lady in an ambulance chair over this rough ground? The ambulance was about 30 miles away. Quite a problem indeed.

The problem could have been increased the next moment as my foot slipped into a ditch at the edge of the path. A lot of help a doctor with a sprained ankle would be in this situation! Fortunately, no harm was done but greater care was taken the rest of the way.

We came down an incline, and suddenly, through scrub and trees, the gable end of a house materialised. It was a one-roomed cottage – cosy and snug with a stove and lamps. After examining the patient, it was clear she wouldn't need hospital admission, so no heroics were going to be required. I was given a welcome cup of tea and then my escort walked back with me to the car.

I was back home by 3.15 am and took morning surgery at 9.00 am. How would I have got her to the tarred road?

Carnage on a mountain side

On a Monday morning in the middle of an outbreak of influenza, I received a call asking if I could visit three men on the working site of Glensanda who had been in bed for two to three days with influenza. I arranged to be met by the Glensanda launch after finishing the surgery on the Isle of Lismore at 4.00 pm. I proceeded to Glensanda and saw the men with influenza and while waiting for the return boat at 5.00 pm was interrupted in discussion by a landrover coming into the yard at high speed. A man jumped out saying that there had been a major accident with contractors putting electricity into the site two miles up the hill. I therefore proceeded as fast as possible up to the ICI factory which is at the end of the road and then on foot across the burn and over the mountain side for about one mile on very slippy, steep terrain – there had been several weeks of hard frost which was just beginning to thaw. We met a sight of utter carnage as the pipe layer had overturned coming down the hill whilst carrying eight men.

The driver's body had been ripped in half and the other seven bodies lay strewn over some 300 yards of the hillside. Immediate attempts to triage were undertaken and an eerie silence prevailed as 180 men looked on in horror at the sight. We arranged for the quarry boat to go offshore to give us radio contact via the boats to the offices down below. A helicopter was scrambled from RAF Leuchars and a lifeboat was launched from Oban. All I had with me was my black bag with three syringes and a small number of ampoules of pethidine and morphine and no intra-venous fluids.

A quick assessment showed one patient with a compound fracture of tibia and fibula; one with a fracture dislocation of shoulder and broken ribs, one with multiple head injuries and an eye removed and covered from head to toe in blood, one with a suspected ruptured spleen and/ or liver, another with a suspected spine injury, another regaining consciousness after being knocked out with no apparent external injuries and the final patient with a closed ankle injury. I allocated workers to stay with each of the seven injured and decided to move the more seriously injured by manned stretchers down to the first aid centre, whilst remaining with the rest of the casualties on the hillside. The lifeboat arrived shortly before the helicopter and as the helicopter came across the Lynn of Morvern there was an almighty explosion down below us. It became apparent that no-one had told the blasters what was happening and the 6.00 pm blast had gone off on time much to the chagrin of the helicopter crew and everyone around. We quickly reassured the helicopter crew that no other explosions were going to happen. The man with a spinal injury was winched off the hill as was the man with a ruptured spleen/liver and both were flown to Glasgow. The suspected spinal injury and lower limb fracture were flown to Oban. The rest of the casualties were transported by lifeboats to Oban.

At 9.30 pm after giving statements to the police, and checking out all the other minor casualties and a quick debrief I returned to Port Appin to finish my routine visits of the day. Thankfully all seven patients made satisfactory recoveries.

A birth to remember

During the 1980s Appin had a large number of New Age Travellers living on the edge of the practice area. Many of them chose to have babies in their caravans, horse boxes and buses. The most memorable of these deliveries was the child of "one-armed Pete", and his partner Mel. Pete was a former member of the Royal Army Medical Corps and wished to deliver his own child but asked for my presence. I was called at the appropriate time to the bus to find Pete lying unconscious on the floor having been hit with a turnip by his partner when she went into transition stage. He lay unconscious throughout the delivery which proceeded relatively uneventfully although accompanied by a choir of some 20 to 25 hippies chanting "Here we go, here we go!" followed after the delivery by "Nice one Mel". Thereafter Pete regained consciousness in time to roll out the barrel of home-brewed beer that he had made for the occasion and great merriment was had by all.

An emergency

I received a phone call from the Ambulance Service saying they had received a 999 call from a phone box on the Island of Lismore. It was from an unidentified person, believed to be a child, saying her father was impaled on railings on the west side of Lismore. They asked if I could help as they had no means of responding. I contacted the District Nurse who had heard nothing and she phoned several points on Lismore and asked individuals to check where we thought there might be railings where there might be someone impaled. We contacted Glensanda to ask for assistance and they immediately released one of their fast boats from ferry duties to help our search and the District Nurse went on the boat down the west side of the island. Foot parties went out from Port Ramsay and from Achnadin, one heading south and one heading north. The local policeman contacted me asking to borrow my car on Lismore, and I explained that I was already involved in the situation and he came and stayed with me in my house and we tried to co-ordinate the information we were getting in.

After an hour and a half my doorbell rang and a visitor asked if I was the doctor because he had scratched his head falling off his bicycle. I explained I was busy with a serious incident on Lismore and his face dropped slightly and said that he had fallen off his bicycle on Lismore. I asked if he had a daughter and he said yes. She had gone to get help and he had not seen her since and it quickly became apparent that this man with a scratch on his forehead was the person who was supposedly impaled on a railing on Lismore. I asked him to wait a second while I nipped in and spoke to the policeman who jumped up and down a couple of times, but when he considered the paperwork that would be necessary for pursuing a charge of wasting police time he asked me just to put an elastoplast on the man's head and preferably give him a kick up the backside and send him on his way. I did the former and refrained from the latter.

Local knowledge

Last summer I was fishing in our boat with my family in the bay in Lochaline, and took the mobile phone for any emergencies. We were returning home with a few mackerel when I saw a small rigid inflatable boat heading towards me. The man aboard asked if I was the doctor, and swiftly raced me across the bay to a dive boat where a diver was having some difficulties. Unfortunately my phone battery had gone flat and no one had been able to contact me. However the local publican had pointed out my boat, and the crew came to fetch me. Patients in such small communities seem to have a second sense in knowing where to find you.

An explosive event

It was our first winter in the practice and suddenly there was a knock at the front door one evening. When I opened the door, a man unknown to me then said "Come quickly, there's been an explosion in the square." With that, he turned round and ran off, leaving me wondering what I was going to face – had the IRA planted a bomb here? How many dead would there be? How much morphine should I take?

What had actually happened was that an elderly couple in the square had lit their fire, which had a back boiler, but the pipes connected to it had been frozen. As the water expanded, there was nowhere for it to go and the back boiler exploded with such force that the outside granite wall was bowed and cracked and the inside of their house looked like a bomb had hit it. There was a bit of smoke and fire and a dazed-looking lady lying in the corner of the room. Her husband had left the room at the time, to answer a call of nature, which was probably his saving. His wife had a broken collarbone and a few burns and was somewhat dazed as you might imagine.

When the boiler had exploded, it had flown across the room and passed through a door leaving a hole in it in the shape of the boiler! It was really like something out of a Tom & Jerry cartoon.

The boiler had then landed amongst a heap of plastic bottles that the gentleman was collecting for some reason, so there was plastic smoke in the air as well. The flight path of the boiler had gone right across the chair in which he had been sitting, which is why his call of nature had been his saving grace.

A stitch in time

It was a beautiful summer's day, in the bad old days when the surgery was attached to the house.

"There's a sheep in the wire over the fence at the back" my wife said. I went to see. Sure enough a ewe had got herself all tangled up in some abandoned barbed wire lying just over the fence.

Super doc to the rescue. My wife held the sheep, while I tried to untangle it but there was no chance. It had struggled so much the fleece was well matted into the barbs and we were getting nowhere.

Who says doctors are not resourceful? I went back over the fence, into the surgery and grabbed a pair of curved scissors from the sterilizer and bob's your uncle, one slightly sheared sheep, but at least free to recount the tale.

Unfortunately, sheep skin isn't like human skin, or maybe it's just that humans are usually anaesthetised and, if not unconscious, trying to co-operate but it just took one nick, maybe a quarter of an inch long and it was like a zipper undoing – eight or ten inches; the whole belly was exposed and it looked like I was trying to gralloch it.

There was panic, but strangely enough no blood – it almost looked like a dissection. Loud shouts to the house brought further assistance to subdue a by now very frightened sheep.

Then it was back over the fence with needle forceps, toothed tissue forceps, 3/0 black silk, ten stitches and some fleece later it was released.

The farmer was never told, and at least the sheep didn't complain to the Health Board.

Breaking the rules

A couple of years ago, a 94-year-old male patient of mine was interviewed on Scottish national television news. He and his wife were the longest married couple in Scotland – a mere 73 years. He was telling the interviewer his secrets of a long and happy married life. He thought Westray was the best place in the world to live and even "had a nice doctor who let him drive even though he couldn't see!" The fact that this was about 500 yards along the length of a field to collect his pension was not explained and I waited with bated breath for my defence union to ring.

Life saving event

I was in the midst of a busy Monday morning surgery when an urgent request for a house call came in from a lady whose husband had collapsed. I dashed out of the clinic leaving a packed waiting room behind me. The house was two to three miles away along narrow country roads and as I zoomed along I was praying that I would not meet any of the local farmers with a muck sprayer!

Thankfully I reached the house safely and found Bill on the kitchen floor, very blue but conscious. I dispatched his wife to my car to collect the oxygen and emergency bag and just then Bill collapsed again. This time there was no pulse and I launched into cardio-pulmonary resuscitation.

However to my great surprise after two respirations and a couple of chest thrusts had been delivered, Bill opened his eyes and was obviously responding. His pulse and breathing became regular and he was able to talk without difficulty and I began to wonder if I had misjudged the situation in the first place.

The ambulance quickly arrived, having covered 19 miles in 17 minutes, and Bill was taken to the local GP hospital. I returned to my surgery and thankfully to a less full waiting room. A short time later I got an urgent phone call from the nursing staff to say that Bill's heart rate had suddenly shot up and that although he was still fully conscious they thought I should come quickly. It transpired that Bill was having spells of ventricular tachycardia and presumably I had witnessed and managed to resuscitate him from an episode of pulseless ventricular tachycardia at home.

He went on to be treated and investigated in the district hospital and from there he was transferred to Glasgow where he underwent insertion of a dual action internal defibrillator.

He returned home from hospital after one month and still remains fit and well. It gives me a great feeling of satisfaction each time I see him out and about to know that this is one life I was privileged to save.

Just in time

Early one morning a mother phoned in great distress saying her baby wasn't breathing. I made my fastest turn out ever and on arrival there was this limp rag-doll and my first impression was – too late. Fortunately after mouth to mouth resuscitation he regained colour quickly. The father drove my car to the hospital while I sat in the back continuing mouth to mouth resuscitation. He turned out to have whooping cough and spent six weeks in hospital. Originally I had not been due on call that night as the rota had been changed. The doctor who would have been on call would have taken much longer to arrive.

It is rare in general practice for seconds to really count, but when there is a successful outcome, it compensates for some of the more mundane day-to-day work.

The authors

Rosie Donovan

Rosie Donovan is a Scottish-born photographer who has lived in Canada since 1972. She studied photography at Beal Art School and the University of Western Ontario. She is a passionate observer of people, capturing the essence of her subjects, meticulously posing them to reflect their personalities, lifestyles and interests. She works exclusively in black and white, using available light. Rosie Donovan's exhibitions have toured extensively. Major venues include The Canadian Museum of Civilization, The Glasgow Royal Concert Hall (for Fotofeis), The Canadian Embassy, Riyadh, Saudia Arabia and the Kelvingrove Art Gallery and Museum.

In this project, forty-seven of the two hundred or so single-handed doctors in Scotland report on their experiences and provide an insight into their unique contributions to rural Scottish health care. In 1998, Rosie Donovan spent six months travelling by Land Rover, from the Rhinns of Galloway in the far southwest, to Unst, the most northerly of the Shetland Isles. She visited doctors working under a wide range of conditions: from small island communities, separated from the nearest hospital by a ferry journey of several hours; to practices which, while only ten miles apart, are separated by a mountain road often impassible in winter.

She recorded interviews with doctors, in which they discussed life as the sole physician in a remote community, their responsibilities to patients as well as their own families, their feelings about this form of medical practice and their hopes for its future. Each chose a favourite location for a photograph which they felt best represented their place of work. There were times when the doctors' busy schedules allowed her little time to get to know them, interview them, record their impressions and experiences of life as a rural doctor, and find a suitable location for a portrait. Sometimes the demands of their practice meant that they could spare as little as half an hour.

At other times, she could spend longer getting to know them, and often, after the work was done, go sailing or hiking in the hills, have lunch or dinner, and meet their families. For her, it was a tremendously rewarding experience, as she gained insight into the lives of these dedicated physicians and made friends for life of many of them. The resulting photographs show them posed against the stunning backdrops of their places of work – some of the most beautiful and rugged areas of Scotland. The accompanying texts illustrate their commitment to single-handed practice as the art of medicine.

photograph by John Rowlands

John Bain

John Bain is Professor of General Practice at the University of Dundee. He is a graduate of Aberdeen University and was formerly in full-time practice in Livingston, West Lothian. Before coming to Dundee he was Professor of Primary Medical Care at the University of Southampton.

He was born and brought up in Aberdeenshire which provided a rural background, and after his experience one summer as a locum GP in the Western Isles has always had an interest in doctors in remote and isolated areas. Many of the students he is now responsible for spend their general practice teaching placements in rural practices which has provided further insight into the work of these doctors.

His hobbies are mainly related to outdoor pursuits, including photography and he was stimulated by Rosie Donovan's exhibition "Ex Patria" which depicted emigrant Scots living in Canada. From that connection came the idea of this book.

In editing the transcripts of interviews with the doctors in this book, it was striking how many common themes emerged, and the importance of the doctor-patient relationship frequently emphasized. Reading these accounts of their work highlighted the need to remind people of the unique characteristics of doctors who have made so many contributions to their communities. At a time when single-handed practice has had less attention than it probably deserves, the core values of medical practice are more than adequately represented by the following texts.

The Northern Islands
Orkney and Shetland

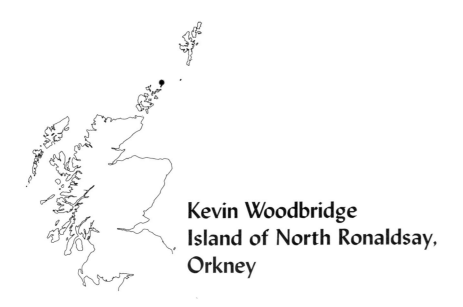

Kevin Woodbridge
Island of North Ronaldsay, Orkney

After graduating, I worked for three years in academic hospital posts and at that time general practice was not a career option. However, I came to think that working in a small rural practice would be ideal and, after a training post in the Hebrides, I was appointed to my present job in 1977.

This is a very small practice on an island four miles by two miles. When I first came here there were 120 patients; there are only 80 now. It's an area where you have to make decisions about whether to get the lifeboat to take a patient to the mainland, or just get on with things yourself. I have walk-in surgeries three days a week and on a Saturday morning, but I also have other interests which keep me fully occupied.

We have a 36-acre croft with North Ronaldsay sheep which are a unique breed. I'm also director of the bird observatory which collects migration data and has been a source of considerable stimulation. We collect all the migration data and I am promoting the use of this data for population monitoring. There is a huge database here which has information about bird movements going back fifty years. I'm also chief fireman on the island and one of the five coastguards. I'm active on the community council and involved in social activities, which keeps me in touch with what people are thinking. There are only four pupils in the local school at present which is the lowest since I've been here. There are now four children under school age including two of my own and the school will be up to eight pupils before the eldest leaves for secondary education in Kirkwall.

Until recently the continuous on-call commitment was a major constraint, but the advent of the Associate Practitioner Scheme has been a major step forward. We are also in the midst of building an aerial for mobile phones and this will improve communication dramatically. Up until now I have had to leave messages about my whereabouts on answering machines; I'll now be able to go out and about without having to worry about how I can be contacted. As you can see I have a lot of outdoor interests and my life certainly doesn't revolve around medicine all the time.

I sat on a local enquiry in the 1980s about the future of medical practice on this island and the conclusion was, that in financial terms, it was still the best option to have a doctor on the island. If you have a nurse practitioner or paramedical service they would require purpose-built premises and some form of medical backup and the investment would not be dissimilar to having a self-employed doctor with an inducement allowance. As long as doctors continue to come to islands like this, then there are strong arguments to maintain the current arrangements. As for myself, I cannot look too far into the future but when the children eventually leave home for higher education then we may have to reconsider our options. Our way of life wouldn't suit everybody but it has provided a rich mixture of interests both within and outwith medical practice.

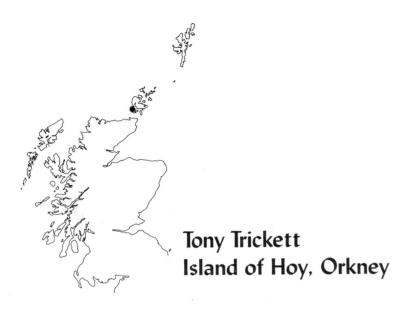

Tony Trickett
Island of Hoy, Orkney

I was originally in single-handed practice in Pembrokeshire but I had 3500 patients and it was just getting too much for me. The place was getting bigger, the motorway was getting closer and I was reaching the stage that to survive I would have to drop my standards. I've been here now for twenty-five years and this is my home, my life and where I shall retire. Longhope is part of the Island of Hoy and my practice is quite small with only 400 patients. The island is thirty miles long and about eight to nine miles wide so I do have to do a bit of travelling when visiting patients at home. I suppose I'm a bit of a rebel and enjoy the freedom of single-handed practice. My patients are all well known to me as I see them all the time; I meet them in the shop, I play badminton with them and I occasionally have a drink with them in the pub. Total patient care and the care of people within their own families is fundamental to my philosophy of general practice. I do both morning and evening surgeries three evenings a week until 7.00 p.m. which may seem quite late, but the boat comes in around then and the shop closes at 7.00 p.m. so it is a convenient time for my patients.

You have to deal with everything here and if you get a message that a patient has collapsed vomiting blood you are already planning the care en route. Organising the ambulance driver, the district nurse, the ferry to transport the patient to the mainland hospital; all these things have to be thought of. Fortunately, I have a radio telephone and a radio pager and mobile phones work well here. There are seldom two emergencies at the same time but the support systems are really good with everyone mucking in together. Getting emergencies off the island could be a problem before the helicopter service which has the advantage that it can land anywhere and there are few situations, other than fog, when it cannot fly. I suppose my proudest moment was receiving the MBE for services to medicine which reminded me that doctors in isolated areas are regarded highly.

I have been involved in all the organisations on the island from the Community Council to school boards. One of the biggest honours of my life was to be appointed to be Honorary Secretary of the Longhope Lifeboat which goes back to 1874. I have trained all the lifeboat men in first aid and the lifeboat service is vitally important to the island. I am also Chairman of the Hoy Trust which is obliged to maintain and preserve ten thousand acres of land which is of extremely high ecological value. It includes several farms and crofts and the Hoy Inn which is a pub at the far end of the island.

Although it can be a tough life, there are tremendous rewards in serving a community like this. I don't really think that a paramedical or flying doctor service would work. The island needs someone to be the central figure in medical care and provide continuity of care to the individuals who become part of your life.

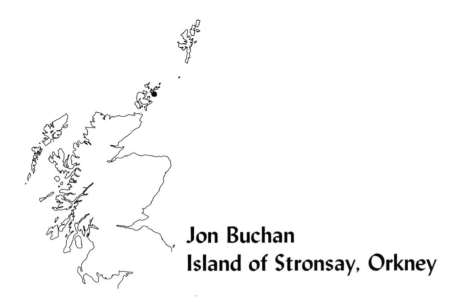

Jon Buchan
Island of Stronsay, Orkney

I've only been here since 1995 and prior to coming had been a Senior Medical Officer in the Civil Service for twelve years, having been in practice for fourteen years before that. I had reached the stage in my life where the Civil Service and I were not really compatible and I needed a change. It was quite a change too! Before coming I had to do some re-training and was a trainee GP in Totton in Southampton. I will never forget the day we arrived here – we had left Southampton at 3.00 in the afternoon and arrived at Scrabster at 5.30 the next morning having driven all night. We then got on the boat to Orkney and then had a crossing via Sanday and Eday before arriving on Stronsay. My wife had never been to the island before but she has taken to it like a fish to water; it is very much like her childhood where she was brought up in a village of around 400 people and she likes the atmosphere of a small community.

It is a very small practice with only 340 patients on an island seven miles long and two miles wide. My wife, who is a nurse, acts as the dispenser in the practice. Although it is a small practice, I am kept busy as there are a lot of elderly people, some of whom are quite poorly. I do around 1500 visits a year – about four to five visits a day. There is this notion that if the doctor turns up and says you are all right then you believe it; very much a kind of lucky charm idea. It may not be considered modern medicine but lots of patients believe it. I had this old chap I used to see every other day because I knew from experience that if I went to see him he stayed all right, but if I didn't visit he would get poorly and send for me. In a community like this you have to forsake ideal medical practice to retain faith with your patients and this is particularly true for older patients.

There are times when the surgery is relatively quiet. For example this morning nobody came to see me at all, while the next day there could be anything between ten and fifteen. It can be a strain being on call all the time but I am not called out very much at night. Finding locums during holiday time is a real problem. You can spend hours on the phone trying to get somebody to come and in the end it is sometimes easier just to stay working than it is to go through all the hassle of getting someone to work as a locum.

I suspect that when I retire I might not be replaced. The island is depopulating and in the last few months alone three families with young children have left. It may be possible to have one doctor for the islands of Stronsay, Sanday and Eday but the doctor would require a boat and be able to handle it. In many ways, a doctor on an island like this ensures that a community remains viable. Without a doctor, even more families would leave which would threaten the future of the island. I'm not suggesting that I am absolutely essential but there may be problems in finding a replacement when I retire.

Shirley Haunschmidt
Island of Westray, Orkney

I was brought up in Essex and after medical school in London did my general practice training in Dartford, Kent. After that I worked for three years in a large group practice in Yorkshire which was not really my cup of tea. After about a year I left and worked part-time in a small practice which I really enjoyed. By this time I was married and had two young children and my husband was also working and we did not see as much of each other as we would have liked. He was not really enjoying his job and when we saw an advertisement for a job in the Orkney Islands we decided that I should apply as we had been to Scotland a lot on holiday and had happy memories of our times there.

We have had two more children since then and it has really been a marvellous place to bring them up. It is very safe: they can walk home from school, the school is excellent, they have a lot of freedom and can wander on their bikes, and I do not have to worry about their safety.

I have 650 patients on an island which is only twelve miles long by five miles wide. However, I also serve the island of Papa Westray which I visit once a week by boat. Despite being on an island, the back-up services are very good and with a daily ferry service to Kirkwall we are not really too isolated. There are no long waiting lists and I have good contact with specialists who recognise the nature of the job I do which gives me a good sense of security.

The patients really appreciate the service and there have been times when I have felt guilty about how undemanding they can be. I remember when I was pregnant and was working right up to two weeks before the baby was born, and people would come in in the morning quite sick and say they could not possibly have called me out because I was pregnant.

At present we have every intention of staying here. Things may change when the children leave primary school to go to the secondary school in Kirkwall but that is for the future. I do not know if I could go back to the routine of a group practice where you have to work set hours with appointments and where patients are much more demanding.

I do not think there is any alternative to having a doctor on the island, and if it was only to be a nursing service then there would have to be shifts of nurses which could be just as expensive as having one doctor. Westray may be safe from any plans to amalgamate services as it is one of the bigger islands in the Orkneys, and with a population of reasonable size keeps someone like me fully occupied most of the time.

Susan Bowie
Hillswick, Shetland

I came to Shetland because I had lots of friends here and I used to work in the fish factory as a student. I kept in touch with these friends who let me know there was a locum job on the island. I came for five years, and after my first son was born I moved to the single-handed practice in Hillswick. That lasted for two years, but I then had to move to Inverness because of my husband's job. After a few years and two children later, we got the chance to return and I became the single-handed practitioner again in Hillswick.

My practice covers a fairly wide area which is characterised by a combination of wilderness and dramatic sea cliffs which have some of the best nesting areas in Britain. There are only 700 patients and one of the really good things about being single-handed is that you know everyone well and they know you.

I'm on call all the time but it is not too busy. I start morning surgery at 9.30 and am usually finished with appointments and home visits by 2.30 in the afternoon. The patients are very good at not calling you out at night; I probably get a night call once every four months and it is usually something serious. They don't call you out for a child with earache in the middle of the night; they wait until the morning.

I really enjoy the way I can work here, having a lot of time for all my patients. I am on first name terms with all of them and they are on first name terms with me. I am also extremely fortunate with my three members of staff. I have a practice nurse who also has a croft, and the lady who does the computing and secretarial work is the wife of the local lawyer and she also looks after sheep. My receptionist is indispensable and is really a practice manager although the Health Board won't upgrade her. I've help from associate GPs from time to time and there is another one coming in a few months which will make a big difference.

My husband is a journalist and works full-time and for two years was working away from home which was difficult in many respects. Over the years I've been fortunate to have very good childminders and I've also got my mother living nearby so she helps out from time to time as well. If the children hadn't been happy, then I wouldn't have carried on, but in general, they are fairly unaffected by my job.

I'm not sure what the future of single-handed practice will be. I still maintain that single practice is how medicine ought to be. It is about the art of medicine, having time for your patients and not being bogged down by audit projects, guidelines and all that paperwork that has bedevilled the Health Service in recent years. For me, this is the ideal way to practice medicine.

David MacFarlane
Bixter, Shetland

I come from Glasgow originally and trained in Dundee, and the circumstances which brought me here were largely due to informal contacts. A friend of mine had worked here and knew one of the GPs who invited me to be a trainee, and I spent a year on Yell which is one of the offshore islands. About eighteen months later I had the opportunity to come and work as a relief practitioner and ended up being appointed to the post in Bixter, where I have been for the last fifteen years.

The practice has now got 1100 patients which has risen from around 900 when I started. Single-handed practice suits my personality in that I like to mould and shape the practice the way I like it to be and do not have to consult lots of partners before getting decisions taken. With a practice of this size it is more efficient to have an appointments system but I also have three branch surgeries at various villages which means that I do not have too many home visits, as patients with non-urgent problems wait until I am doing one of my surgeries in their village. I know my patients very well now and they seldom call me out at night, and are frequently happy to accept telephone advice as they know they can get an appointment first thing the next morning. There is a local hospital eighteen miles away where there are two consultant surgeons and two consultant physicians, all of whom provide a very good service. I am the honorary medical adviser to the lifeboat service which involves me looking after the crew and attending to casualties.

Most of my social life centres around visiting friends and inviting friends for a meal. There are lots of indoor activities during winter and in the summer, rowing and sailing are quite popular. Outwith the practice I have become involved in medical politics and am the secretary of the local medical committee which results in my representing the Shetland GPs at national committees in Edinburgh. Getting away from the island to go to meetings in Edinburgh keeps me in touch with the outside world but I am always happy to come back.

I think there will be potential problems with recruitment to single-handed practice in the future. One of the deficiencies in training young doctors is that they get little if any exposure to the kind of practice I work in and may not know what they are missing. I think it is very important that students and trainee practitioners should have the opportunity to spend some time in an isolated rural practice like this. I grew up in an urban environment and always thought that I would end up working in a city but circumstances were such that I was exposed to a practice in Shetland. I am very thankful for that, with no regrets whatsoever and would not trade places with anyone.

Mike McDonnell
Island of Yell, Shetland

I came to Yell in 1973 to take over the single-handed practice of Yell and Fetlar, which is about 100 square miles with a population of 1200 people. In my work, there has been enormous satisfaction in knowing my patients well. I do not subscribe to the theory that familiarity breeds contempt and that you lose your objectivity if you are mixing with patients socially. In many ways you are better placed to pick things up, see the early warning signs and notice that someone is behaving out of character.

When you practice and live within the same community it confers on you a degree of accountability that you wouldn't otherwise have, and when you get tuned in to what local concerns are you can play a part in not just developing medical services but looking at wider issues within the community. This has been one of the most egalitarian communities I have ever come across, which has given me freedom to develop in all sorts of ways which has benefited me as a person as well as a doctor.

The drawback of single-handed practice is that you are completely on your own and it is difficult to keep up to date when you are practising in professional isolation. I got around this by becoming a recognised trainer which means that I had responsibility for the training of young doctors. As a trainer for eighteen years it has been a great source of satisfaction that eight of my former trainees have opted for single-handed practice in the Highlands and Islands of Scotland. Those in ivory towers in the mainland need to relax some of their more rigid regulations to allow the growth of single-handed training practices, because it is such an obvious way of solving the problem of future recruitment.

After twenty-five years in my current post I was faced with the prospect of giving up being a trainer as you are not allowed to be one after the age of sixty. I thought it would be a great pity if, after years of building up the practice to be a training practice, it would lose this status if I carried on working full-time. Two younger GPs who had worked in the practice expressed an interest in returning to Shetland, and I thought it was a good time to stand down. It means that the practice can probably continue to be a training practice, thus contributing to the recruitment in remote areas of Scotland. I have taken a post as a part-time associate GP which frees me up to get more involved in community development projects in which I have dabbled over the years.

Unlike some of the 'doom and gloom merchants', I think there is a bright future for rural practice. The ability of single-handed doctors to have an associate has brought relief from the burden of constantly being on call. It also provides a degree of choice for patients and if our medico-political colleagues can ensure that training opportunities are maintained, then practices like the one I have worked in can continue to attract bright and committed doctors.

Rosie Briscoe and Mark Aquilina
Island of Yell, Shetland

I was born in Yorkshire and my husband, who is also a doctor, is from Surrey. After we qualified we worked for a couple of years in Australia, then worked in Shetland before going to Namibia with the Voluntary Services Overseas organisation. We decided that the Shetland Isles was a good place to settle and bring up a family and that is how we ended up here. The previous doctor set up a good practice and was a trainer and we plan to continue with the tradition of being a training practice. I am not single-handed in the strictest sense of the word because my husband and I job-share which means that we can handle the responsibility of 1100 patients together. There are also around 80 patients on the Island of Fetlar and surgeries are held there every two weeks. There is also an associate who works in the practice and the Associate Practitioner Scheme has really revolutionised the life of rural GPs who had previously been on call for months at a time. We divide up the days which, with two children aged four and two years, means that we have time to spend with them.

One of the advantages of our job-sharing arrangement is that patients have the choice of a male or female doctor. I do not know if I would like to be truly single-handed and all on my own. The number of night calls is not onerous but you always have to be available. One thing we like about working in a remote place is that you have more clinical challenges and have to do your own casualty work, and have to manage certain patients who, in city practices, would be passed on to specialists. There is no airstrip on the island so emergencies have to be evacuated by ferry, and you have to be sure that you are calling out the ferry for a good reason.

Having patients as friends has not been as much of a problem as I thought it might be, and we insist that friends or work colleagues who require medical advice make proper appointments and are not handled in a casual way during social encounters. You have to enjoy being part of a rural community and not feel too threatened by it; you can't be too obsessed about your own personal privacy; you just have to become part of the community and get on with it.

The only thing I really miss are trees, because any attempts to grow trees in this wild landscape have been thwarted by the high winds. Otherwise this is a pleasant place to live and we enjoy canoeing and kayaking in the summer and although the winters can be long and dark, the associate scheme enables us to take off the occasional week when we have a blitz on restaurants, theatres and the cinemas on the mainland.

I cannot see any alternative for providing medical care on islands like this because it is quite a long way to the main centre in Lerwick. I agree with those who suggest that medical students should have more experience of remote practices which would influence their future career options and ensure that what has been built up here over many years can be maintained and developed.

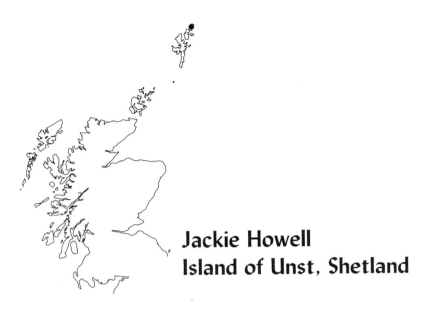

Jackie Howell
Island of Unst, Shetland

Unst is the northernmost practice in Shetland. I have been in single-handed practice here for just over two years. Before that I had been an associate between two of the Shetland practices, and as my husband was away, had to commute between two islands with a small child and a granny. That was a good introduction to the community, as having a child and a granny are good ways to introduce yourself to a lot of people. I think the situation here is probably unique in that my husband Chris is the part-time associate and he works for me ten days a month. Between us we are on call twenty-four hours a day, seven days a week. There are just under 800 people registered in the practice, and the sort of things I see in the practice are fairly standard really, everything from major crises, heart attacks etc., down to the usual childhood ailments. We have some rare endocrine problems around the island: someone with Cushing's Syndrome and someone who has had a pituitary tumour and has all the problems associated with that.

I enjoy single-handed practice but there are disadvantages. The main one is just never being able to go off the island. We're very much part of the community and enjoy that. The children go to the local toddler group and the local school. We all shop at the same shop, swim in the same pool, and go to the same evening classes, dances and weddings; but there are problems involved in having close friends who are also one's patients. Fortunately they're very healthy – I don't see them very often in the surgery.

The part of the island that is accessible by road is about twelve miles by two miles. It is a ten minute ferry ride from the next island, and a two hour journey by road and two ferries to the nearest town, hospital, bank and supermarket, so it is fairly remote. I'm used to the isolation now, although sometimes in bed at night when there is a storm, I worry about the fact that really, under these circumstances, there is practically no way off the island. So if somebody did get very ill, it would be a major problem, which I find quite frightening because it is my responsibility.

I think the future of single-handed practice in Scotland is probably rather uncertain. In a situation like an island practice, I really don't see – and I have thought about this a lot – how they can get round the problem of people needing access to medical services on the island. However, I'm sure that people can argue that it's very expensive per head of population. I think people in rural areas expect to have access to a doctor, and would be fairly angry if that was removed. The nature of practice has already changed and I think will go on changing, but I can't see it not existing in twenty, thirty, or even forty years time. I hope.

The North
Lybster
Bonar Bridge
Lairg
Cromarty
Helmsdale
Canisbay

The North-East

Edzell

Tomintoul

Strathdon

Tarland

Torphins

Buckie

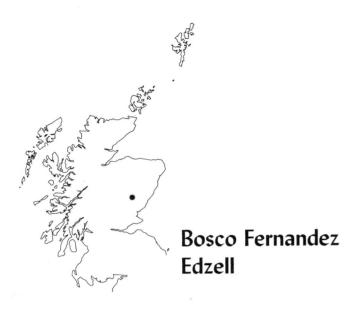

Bosco Fernandez
Edzell

I qualified in Madras in 1960 and came to Britain in 1972. I was lucky when the senior partner of this practice retired and I became a single-handed practitioner, because I have a very independent nature. I find that in single-handed practice I can practice medicine to its fullest by myself. Group practices are all right in cities and other places where populations float and doctors do not come to know their patients very well, but in rural areas people need care in a different sort of way, much more individual care. You come to know your patients well, and we have a mutual trust; they trust me and I trust them, and it makes me give them my all, both in medicine and in empathy in a relationship which is more of a friend than a doctor. There is a lot of satisfaction, because, at the end of the day, you treat that family from their births to their deaths. I find it very satisfying, and a wee word of thanks always makes it wonderful. You find that the patients appreciate this, particularly in the rural areas; they don't come to you for any trivial thing but only when it is really needed.

I hope this will continue to be a single-handed practice because people here need a doctor. Being a scattered population, people would be put to a lot of hardship, particularly the children, if they had to travel ten to fifteen miles to go to a practice or to hospitals which are thirty to forty miles away. I think single-handed practices should be left alone and continue to be funded and maintained. If they close, the only reason I think would be for the sake of saving some money, but what price is human life? That's the way I would like it.

Edzell is a beautiful village which usually wins the Scotland in Bloom competition every year. It has a population of about 900 and my practice number is about 1600, so the rest of the families are scattered around the district with a radius of about ten miles and two glens, Glen Lechler and Glen Esk, which are both beautiful glens.

My main hobby is gardening, and we actually started, where I live, with a bad patch full of weeds and nothing else and we built it up. My wife particularly loves gardening and I help her a lot with it. We have an open day in Edzell for gardens and we have opened our garden to the public. Edzell Castle is maintained by Mr Davidson, the chief gardener, and I was lucky sometimes to have him come along and help me out with my garden.

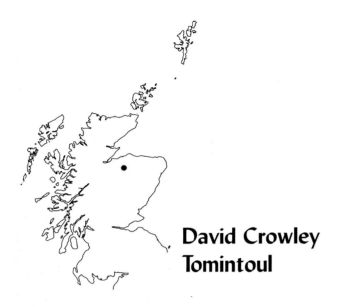

David Crowley
Tomintoul

I did my undergraduate training in London and was originally in a dispensing rural practice north of Rugby in Warwickshire. I've now been here for fourteen years and have enjoyed it immensely. Although Tomintoul is only sixty-five miles from Aberdeen, it is a very remote area which tends to get cut off in the winter months when the exposed Lecht road gets blocked with snow quite frequently.

This is a scattered rural community surrounded by hills with about 500 patients, but it can be busy in the winter months with skiing injuries at the nearby ski slopes and in the summer there are quite a lot of tourists. When we first came, the doctor's consulting room, waiting room and dispensing area were all situated in the house and it was very cramped. There was no soundproofing and patients in the waiting room could tell when I was coming to the end of a consultation because they would say, "He's talking about the weather now." It is changed days now with purpose-built premises across the road with facilities for a triple duty nurse, a practice nurse and part-time physiotherapist and chiropodist. It is only recently that there has been an ambulance based here – before that it was just someone who could drive and had no medical training which could be a bit worrying when you had to send seriously ill people to Aberdeen on a wild winter's night. Having a part-time associate is also very helpful as it does cut down on the amount of time I have to be on call. Having said that, patients here are very considerate and don't call you at night unless it is something serious.

The community life has changed quite drastically since we have been here; there used to be numerous things going on, with a drama club, a bridge club, a bowling club and a shooting club and almost every night of the week there was something to do. Things have changed in that there seem to be fewer community activities. Losing our local school was a big blow although it doesn't affect us now as it happened after our children left to go to university. The high costs of running a garage have also led to the demise of our local garage and all these things continue to undermine the community.

My time outside medicine is spent in outdoor pursuits including long-distance running, cross-country skiing and mountain hiking. Being twenty miles from the next practice and hemmed in by the hills in an area which stretches to the Cairngorms, I don't see any alternative to providing medical services here. Telemedicine and video links may reduce the number of visits that patients have to make to specialist outpatient centres, but there will always be a need for a doctor on site and I look forward to being that doctor for the foreseeable future.

Janet Fitton
Strathdon

I was a medical student at Cambridge University and Charing Cross and Westminster Medical School in London. When I did my general practice training my intention was to work in and around London but my husband-to-be and I both enjoyed outdoor activities including hill walking, camping and getting into the countryside at weekends. I applied to become an associate in this area, and we bought a cottage and planned to stay two or three years. After about a year, the doctor in the practice I'm now in resigned and I was appointed to his post.

There are 670 patients in the practice which consists of the whole of the Strathdon area which goes from Mossat up to the Lecht where there is a skiing centre. There is no main centre of population, with the practice at Bellabeg roughly half way along the glen. I have a part-time associate and I don't think I would have considered single-handed practice without the associate scheme.

Mobile phones don't work here so I do have a lot of time when I have to be at the end of a telephone. I'm hoping that is going to improve soon which means that I would be able to get out and about a bit more and be more involved in the community. My husband now acts as practice manager and has taken over the business side of the practice and I also have two part-time receptionists and a part-time practice nurse. It is also a dispensing practice and we distribute all the patients' drugs as the nearest pharmacy is twenty miles away. We've a boy of one year and I was lucky enough to have a locum provided during my maternity leave. My husband, being part-time, can take a lot of his work home and we have a neighbour who comes in a few mornings a week to help out.

I like this area very much; it is very friendly; there is a long-standing population of farming people and some people with small estates. There is also the well known Lonach Highland Gathering which takes place every summer and everybody turns out for that. With it being a small practice, I know who people are, who they are related to, their families – it is a true family practice. There is some uncertainty about the future with the formation of local health co-operatives which will cover larger areas and populations. I'm a bit apprehensive about going into a larger group as I don't think you will know the patients so well. People have also spoken about nurse practitioners using telemedicine with video links, but I can't imagine how that would work in emergency situations. If there is a medical emergency or road accident I usually get there before the ambulance. We have no plans to move elsewhere; we have recently bought a house. I like the people and the work, and although there are times when I feel somewhat isolated, the advantages of working here far outweigh the disadvantages.

David Starritt
Tarland

I grew up in Wales and went to medical school in London, and after doing my general practice in South Wales came here in 1985. Tarland is called an inducement practice where we are guaranteed our income, as the list size of 750 patients would not be financially viable without a form of inducement.

When we came here we made two public rooms in our house into the consulting room and the waiting room which became a bit of a problem as children came on the scene. We eventually built a new surgery using local tradesmen and that has made a big difference. There was also a chemist in the village at that time and when she announced that she was going to retire, I thought I'd be responsible for all dispensing of prescriptions. However, my wife was a pharmacist; she decided to buy the chemist shop, so now she is the local chemist and I am the local doctor.

Being in a small community we get to know patients really well and if I fancy a beer, I'll go to the pub occasionally and have a drink. By mixing with people in the village I get to know what is going on in the community and at the local school. It is a very safe place for the children to grow up and the surrounding countryside is beautiful.

The main disadvantage of working here used to be the restriction of being on call all the time, although people here do not abuse the system and seldom call you out unnecessarily. More recently I have joined a rota with two other practices in the area which means I am only on one night in five and I can get some weekends with the family. A more difficult problem is getting locums at short notice for short periods and I well remember when our second baby was due I had to arrange for three different doctors to cover various parts of the day so that I could get away. Planning ahead for locums is not so much of a problem, but for unexpected events or illness it can be a bit of a headache.

While this is a rural setting we are only thirty-two miles from the city of Aberdeen, which is an advantage to both us and our patients. I doubt if they will replace me here when I retire as there are more and more moves towards co-operatives and I am sure the health authority must question the cost effectiveness of maintaining a single-handed practice like this. Not being too isolated and with a neighbouring practice around five miles away it is likely that they would organise a branch surgery. However, my retirement is some way off, and I have no intention of moving so they will have to put up with me for some time yet.

Iain McNicol
Port Appin

I've been the doctor here for the last eighteen years having taken over from my father who was here for the previous fifteen years. I enjoy single-handed practice as a way of life because it can be both varied and fulfilling. It may be difficult to get away from the practice but there are so many happy mixes of roles that you can play in the community.

I'm married with four children who went to the local primary school until they were twelve before going to the high school in Oban. It can be a hard life for the family of rural doctors because there are not many teenagers for your children to mix with and play sport. They also live in the shadow of my role because I am known by everybody in the community and I think it was difficult for them to lead their own lives in the community.

One of my main interests has been the Appin Community Co-operative, of which I was the founding chairman and we bought over the village shop when it was threatened with closure. We now run a craft shop and have set up a community trust and community enterprise group which can stimulate the local economy.

In medical practice I am involved in an emergencies care scheme called BASICS which ensures that doctors far removed from accident and emergency centres can provide immediate care in emergency situations. I also take part in a project studying travelling people who have lived in this area since they were dispossessed after Culloden, and there are records which show family trees going back to 1820 with eight generations of intermarriage. There are at least seven genetic diseases among these families and we are trying to address some of the problems that arise from these. It can be quite difficult because the travellers seek comfort from folk of their own kind by intermarrying and tend to turn a blind eye to our suggestions about the dangers.

I think one of the strongest arguments for keeping doctors in rural areas is the focus, the cement as it were, upon which a community can be built. Ministers are covering wider and wider parishes and becoming less a part of individual communities, and teachers no longer live locally. I think we can persuade our political masters that rural practice is worth preserving, as communities tend to value their local doctor rather than being part of a large group where patients don't know who their doctors really are.

Shina Young
Arisaig

I've always been a single-handed practitioner. I went to Kinlochleven in 1972 and was there for five years. I found it very hard – a list of 1200 patients, with a lot of respiratory illness in people who had worked for many years in the British Aluminium factory. I resigned from that when I got married and left general practice for a while when the children were born.

I came to Arisaig in 1989. People whom I knew in the village phoned me up and urged me to apply for this job. We've been here for about nine years now and I'm very happy and settled. My practice list is about 600 and the practice extends from the River Morar in the west through Arisaig and Lochailort and then down towards Glenuig. The surgery is attached to the house; we have hopes for a new surgery being built within the village and that would give us greater facilities and more scope as the present surgery is very cramped. We use our dining room as the office so it will make a big difference when a new surgery is built and we have a bit more privacy in the house. This is a very busy area in the summer time as there are wonderful beaches and scenery with a lot of caravan sites in the area. We see a vast number of temporary residents in the summer with a wide range of medical problems. One day a week I go to Glenuig and do a surgery there which is held in the village hall. It's better than it used to be because I used to see people at the Post Office or even by the roadside or all sorts of strange places like that.

Good family practice is what people really want, because there is a large amount of personal contact with families – often three or four generations in this part of the world. The main disadvantage is the lack of off-duty time. You may not be very busy but are restricted by four to six nights a week on call. Before my husband died, he used to take calls for me when I was out on call. My teenage daughters have done this in recent years, and when my younger daughter goes away I don't really know what I'm going to do. A new system of communication will be required then.

As a single woman general practitioner you certainly need good domestic help as you juggle the responsibilities of home and practice life. I am involved in the local church and I'm also one of the trustees of the village hall. Surprisingly, I don't sail because I get seasick quite easily. Going out in a lifeboat is quite difficult for me. People in rural areas are entitled to a good standard of medical care. I recognise that practices like this are very expensive to run, yet they are essential with the nature of the area and the lack of public transport. Despite the uncertainties and the demands of the job I love Arisaig and intend staying here.

Maris Buchanan
Salen

When I was a medical student I had hoped that I would eventually be in practice in a rural area. I was originally in partnership for about five years in Kyle of Lochalsh and have now been here for five years.

My practice covers a large area from Loch Linnhe in the east to the end of the Ardnamurchan peninsula in the west. I have one main surgery at Salen and branch surgeries at Strontian, ten miles from here and at Kilchoan, twenty miles west. There are about 1100 patients which is quite large for a single-handed practice and it is also a dispensing practice so I'm kept fairly busy. Single-handed practice is a way of life and you have to accept that. I have an associate GP working with me which gives me some time off and this makes a big difference.

I was lucky to be able to appoint two people as practice managers to do all the administrative work and to help with the dispensing. I think this practice may eventually need two doctors as the list size is growing and there are plans for a new high school at Strontian which may bring extra people to the village. I also have help in the house and garden and someone to help me with shopping and cooking. There are no supermarkets nearby and the local shop is limited in what it can provide. If I have plenty of help and plan in advance, I can be well organised when visitors come.

General practice is experiencing difficulties in recruitment in rural areas and this practice is no exception. I have had quite long spells in the last few years without an associate. Without an associate, I need to have locum cover when I am away and, as this is not an inducement practice, I do not receive any additional remuneration for locums. I receive the same out-of-hours allowance as all other practices, and so the payment I receive for being on call for long calls is negligible. However, a lot of the time the on-call commitment is not too great; weekends in winter can be quite quiet, night calls average about one per week over the whole year and we often have long spells with very few night calls. The situation changes in the summer when we have a lot of holiday makers in the area. It has become clear to me over the years that I must travel at all times prepared to deal with emergencies as they arise. It is essential to be well organised so that I can co-ordinate everything effectively for the rapid and safe treatment in transport of patients. I've taken extended training in emergency care as you never know when you are going to be faced with one in this part of the world.

I try to go along to community activities such as concerts and the art exhibition and I do quite a lot of walking. There is a lot going on in this area but I am limited in the extent to which I can take part. I would like to be more involved, but some things are in the evenings when I have surgeries and my on-call commitments mean that I have to be near the phone. Mobile phones and pagers do not work very well here and therefore my social and free time activities are restricted. Despite these inconveniences, I enjoy my work here and if the workload doesn't get too much I hope to stay on.

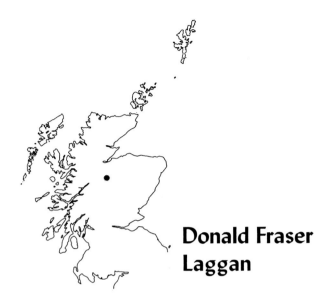

Donald Fraser
Laggan

After I graduated I did my first hospital post in Inverness and then joined an urban practice in Ayrshire which I hated and stayed for only three months. I returned to the Highlands and was a trainee in Fort Augustus and an assistant in Kingussie for a year. At that time it was difficult to get a job and we emigrated to Canada where I worked in rural practice for three years. However our roots were in Scotland and we returned home and I've been in this practice for twenty-one years.

One of the things about this job is that it is not really single-handed – it is a partnership between the doctor and his wife. I can understand why a lot of doctors' wives leave them; it's a full-time job being married to a single-handed doctor. Although there are only 500 patients here I'm kept fairly busy. The next practice is twelve miles away, and although that doesn't sound far, it can be a problem in the winter months. The roads are narrow and twisting and public transport is not always readily available. I can get to places in my Range Rover which other vehicles can't. During one particular period of bad weather I was visiting a

woman which was a four-hour round trip; I would leave the house, drive for twelve miles until I got to the highway, then drive another twelve miles in deep snow and then down a back road for two miles: two hours to get there and two hours to get back. In the winter I used to carry cross-country skis in my car along with food and a sleeping bag, but the winters recently have not been so bad. However, there was a recent occasion, about eight weeks ago, when I was driving in a whiteout and the driving conditions were as bad as I had been in for a long time. It's not nice getting stuck in a blizzard.

There are times when you can feel very isolated in that many people don't really see you as a person, they see you as a doctor. I became aware of this when I decided to build my own surgery and a large section of the community fought me tooth and nail about the land I wished to acquire. Since then I have participated less in community affairs, although in the last year I've started to get involved again. When I came initially, I took it as part of the job to adopt a leadership role and I was the one who organised our own private transmitter when there was no TV in the area. I just accepted it because if you didn't do it, nobody else would.

The stresses of the job can present problems. I thought that we would probably have been quite happy to stay here for the rest of our lives but now I'm not so sure. The winters are hard and long and there are times when I'm tempted to think of retiring to sunnier climes.

Geoffrey Headden
Kinlochleven

I started my life as a GP in an old mining town north of Newcastle Upon Tyne and spent twelve years there. There came a point where I wanted to reduce my workload and run my own business. In the event, I was the only applicant for my current post and this may have been due to the fact that single-handed practice appeals to a relatively small number of doctors who can develop their own pace of work and lifestyle. I was quite surprised nobody else wanted the job. I will never forget the interview as it was in winter with snow and freezing fog delaying the long journey to Inverness.

The advantage to the people living here is that they have a doctor who is available within the village. They don't have to travel up to twenty miles for medical care and they also come to know me as a friend. I can be quite busy and the night-call commitment certainly restricts your social life. This is one of the larger single-handed practices with around 1000 patients and I dispense all their medications. Most of the patients with chronic conditions don't go to hospital outpatient clinics as I provide the continuity of care for them, which is different from a city practice where a lot of patients are followed up in hospital. There are quite a lot of social problems with uncertainty about employment which causes difficulties for people who may have to uproot themselves to find a job.

Although the practice list size may not appear too large compared to a city practice, it is not really comparable to a similarly sized practice in a town. I have to do the dispensing of medicines, suture wounds which elsewhere would probably be referred to hospital, and cope with tourists in the summer who add significantly to the workload.

I am keen on setting myself quality standards and am trying to put together a practice plan for the next two years which might include reviewing my care of patients with chronic illness like asthma and diabetes. It can be difficult to push yourself to maintain high standards because there aren't any other medical colleagues noting what you are doing.

I don't find that I get involved too much with the community although I joined the social club to ensure that there are enough people to justify its existence. My wife tends to have more involvement with community affairs than I have and she is a lieutenant in the Girls Brigade. I don't know if I will stay here permanently; my wife and I have talked about some sort of missionary work before we are too old. We have two sons aged thirteen and fifteen and they will need to finish their education before we think of moving. For the foreseeable future I see myself staying here in Kinlochleven.

75

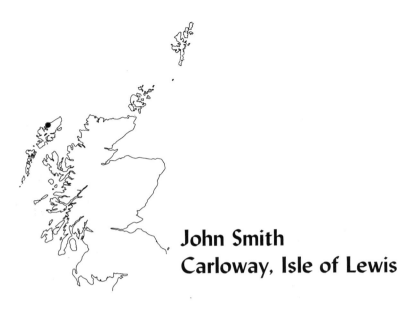

John Smith
Carloway, Isle of Lewis

I was born in the west of the Island of Lewis some six miles south of where I am now practising, so it's an area where I've spent the whole of my life. I was originally in practice in Stornoway for nearly twenty years, but in 1991 I was looking for some new challenges and direction in my life. The government had just introduced what is called the Associate Practitioner Scheme whereby single-handed practitioners qualify for additional part-time help which provides time off and night cover. I also have a registrar, who is a young doctor in training, and I am an examiner with the Royal College of General Practitioners, which forces me to read the medical journals and keep up to date.

I've around 1300 patients in a dispensing practice and I work approximately two weeks on and one week off when my associate covers my work. The people here are very undemanding and will sometimes delay seeking help to the detriment of their own health. An example of this was a lady who phoned me up one morning and asked if I could visit her the next time I was in the area. She was complaining of pains in her chest, and alarm bells were ringing in my head as she was someone who seldom complained. I arranged to see her almost immediately, and her electro-cardiogram showed that she had signs of a heart attack which needed fairly urgent attention. She commented on the fact that she thought that was what it was last night when the pain started, but thought it was far too wild a night to call me out, and wouldn't dream of sending for me in the middle of the night. She was prepared to wait until I was available; not demand an immediate visit which would have been quite justified. You also have to be prepared to deal with all kinds of emergencies as the nearest hospital is twenty-five miles away along narrow twisting roads. Three quarters of my consultations with patients are in Gaelic, the older people being more comfortable with their native language rather than English.

My main hobby is playing the bagpipes and I am involved in the local piping society where I try to promote an interest among the younger generation who can maintain the tradition of playing the pipes. I am also chairman of the board of directors of a local arts organisation which is attempting to raise five million pounds for a purpose-built centre, which will help sustain longstanding traditions. I also have a boat here and do a lot of fishing although I have only caught one salmon this year but caught some fresh herring two nights ago. I can't think of any other place I would like to be working, and as long as my health remains good I will continue to live and work here.

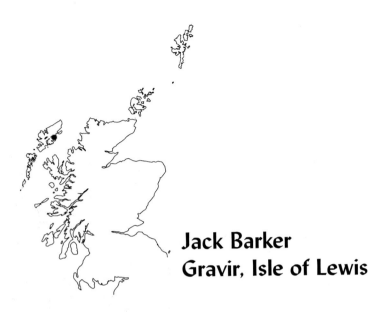

Jack Barker
Gravir, Isle of Lewis

I was in the Royal Air Force for twenty years, first as an ear, nose and throat surgeon and then in general medical duties. My last but one posting was as a senior medical officer at Kinloss in Morayshire and I was active in general practice with around 3000 families as well as 2500 RAF personnel to look after. When working in Scotland I had done locums in the Western Isles for quite a long time and I knew some of the doctors in Stornoway. I decided to leave the RAF and within a month was appointed to this practice; that was seventeen years ago and I have never really regretted the move.

It is a very small practice with around 400 patients which means that it is an inducement practice whereby I receive an allowance to make it financially viable to work here. I also share an associate with one of the doctors on the other side of the island. This gives me the opportunity to share problems and also provides much needed time off which was not the case in the past. My wife acts as the practice manager and there are two part-time receptionists who have taken a variety of qualifications to keep themselves up to date. There is also a district nurse and physiotherapist, occupational therapist and community psychiatric nurse who have responsibilities for a variety of practices including my own. When I think of it, the population here is very well provided for in terms of medical services.

The practice population is getting older all the time with eighty patients, which is about twenty percent of the practice, over the age of eighty years. However, there has been a shift recently with younger people coming back to the islands. Fish farming has been quite successful and the roads are now much better than they used to be. When I came here it used to take about an hour and a half to get to Stornoway which was the nearest town. That journey can now be made in forty minutes.

We used to live in the house to which the surgery was attached but eventually built our own home on a promontory overlooking the sea loch. I now have two thirds of an acre of very exposed land where I am trying to create a garden. My other hobby is fly-fishing for trout and salmon and this is an ideal area for indulging in interests like fishing.

I suspect they will try and amalgamate this practice with a neighbouring practice when I retire, although attempts to do this will be bitterly resented. People here cherish their independence, and they also value services such as the local doctor and local school; they see these services as the cement which holds the community together. Medical services cannot be seen in isolation from the infrastructure required to maintain a sense of community, and people who choose to live in isolated areas deserve to have readily accessible medical care.

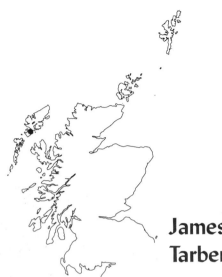

James Finlayson
Tarbert, Isle of Harris

My origins are in the Highlands, my family is from Skye and I was born and brought up in Newtonmore. Although I've no close relatives here, I understand the culture because I really feel that I am one of them. I was originally going to be a psychiatrist but I had been a trainee in the practice and when my trainer offered me a partnership I jumped at the chance to live and work in the Western Isles. After he retired I had a partner for about three years and since he left, I have been single-handed with the help of an associate during the last few years.

This is a large practice for one doctor with 1500 patients, but it is a dying community with around twenty to forty deaths a year and only ten to twelve births. There are 340 patients in Scalpay which used to be an island but there is now a bridge across to it. In days gone by, there was a district nurse based there and she would see all the problems and call you across if she was in any difficulty. You had to arrange the ferry and going over at night under the starlit sky is a distinct memory but it is now part of the mainland which doesn't have the same attraction.

Fishing is declining and Harris Tweed is almost out of existence so that there are no real employment opportunities apart from fish farming. The tourist industry is quite small and hasn't really taken off which may be due to the gales and storms that we tend to get out here.

The thing I really enjoy about single-handed practice is the opportunity to see an interesting problem through to its conclusion and not having to depend on specialist help. I also like working with a very close team and the relationship with everybody who works in the practice brings a lot of job satisfaction. My wife is the relief nurse and secretary and enjoys being part of the extended family of the practice.

The main disadvantage is being on call at night and I think it would be quite a good life if you could relax at night knowing you were going to have a good night's sleep. The creation of the Associate Practitioner Scheme has been a tremendous improvement but even with an associate I am sometimes on call continuously for up to four weeks. With no mobile phones or radio pagers, you have to be available at all times and the days have gone when a single-handed GP could go off for a bit of fishing or sailing and not be contacted for a few hours.

There will have to be changes to allow people to have more protected time and it may be that there will be fewer single-handed doctors in the future. That is not to say that I haven't enjoyed my time here which has been extremely rewarding.

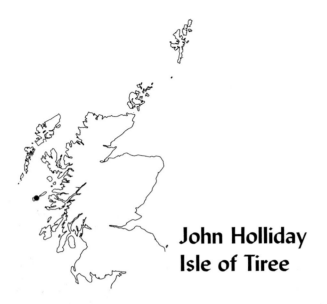

John Holliday
Isle of Tiree

I was born in Essex, spent most of my youth in Norfolk, and after studying science at Cambridge University, went on to study medicine in London. I've always had an interest in remote places and I spent a number of years looking after aboriginal people at Kintore, an isolated practice in Australia, about 800 kilometres from Alice Springs. My son was born in Alice Springs Hospital but we decided we couldn't live there long-term. When we came back to this country I couldn't settle down, but I then got the chance to come to Tiree. I'd gone on holiday on several occasions to the north west of Scotland and my first hospital post after graduating had been in Fort William. The island of Tiree is about twelve miles long and about two to three miles wide and although I only have 750 patients, I do a lot of driving to visit people at home. I'm extremely happy working here; the people are very polite and undemanding. You'll get a patient coming in on a Monday morning and saying they had chest pain all weekend, or had an epileptic fit on Saturday night but did not want to call me out at the weekend.

The size of the practice is a balance between being small enough to spend time with patients but large enough to be presented with the usual variety of medical problems. You have to keep on your toes and there are exciting times when the plane can't get in and you have to manage burns, set fractures and do minor surgery which would otherwise have to go to hospital. One of the features of the island is that there is a good air service to Glasgow which is where I tend to refer patients requiring hospital care. I don't get very much time off and even with the Associate Practitioner Scheme I find myself just finishing seven weeks on call before getting a break.

The Gaelic language is still quite strong among the older people and I have worked at becoming reasonably fluent in the language. My wife and children both speak Gaelic but don't use it very much. I have a lot of interests outside medicine, with music being particularly important to me. I co-founded a traditional music teaching festival which now is in its tenth year and we have about a 100 children attending every year. They are taught a mixture of musical instruments, dancing and singing and it has helped a revival of traditional music and arts on the island. My main passion at the moment is setting up a museum to reflect the history of the island and we have raised money to buy a building so that people who visit here can learn about the island's traditions.

The South West Highlands

Muasdale
Southend
Tarbert
Tighnabruaich
Isle of Arran
Isle of Islay
Drummore

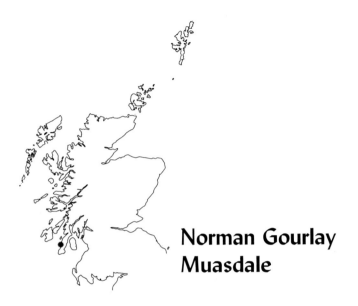

Norman Gourlay
Muasdale

I came to Scotland looking for a single-handed post in a rural area because I really didn't want to have partners any more; I quite wanted to do my own thing. One came up here at Muasdale which was roughly what I was looking for: a single-handed practice. I could run my own show; what I earned was what I'd done and I didn't have to discuss with other people how I wanted to develop or change the practice. Being independent was part of it. Some of it was wanting to do old fashioned medicine: having my own patients, the patients knowing me, forming a relationship with the patients. That latter bit hasn't worked out perfectly because we can't easily do seven days a week and it's this difference between continuous care and continuity of care where you can't be available to your patients all the time, although here we are more often than not.

I've been here eight years now and we had a new surgery built recently which has changed our way of practice. We've also taken on GP training which is unusual for such a small practice and that is something that keeps you alive. We are a dispensing practice; we wouldn't be able to make average earnings if we didn't dispense, and our patients would be horrified if they had to pick up a prescription from here and then go to get it honoured in a chemist's shop. I think that the essence of general practice is that you should go to a place and stop, and build up a knowledge of your patients and their families, but the downside of rural practice is that you're very much in a goldfish bowl all the time, in that everybody in this area is my patient and I'm everybody's doctor. The people don't have a choice of doctor and I don't have a choice of patients.

Although in balance I prefer country life, it's slightly strange for a city boy like me. I still have my flat in Glasgow and we go there to look for pavements and shops and the university and other things that keep your mind ticking over. I'm also doing a theology honours degree in Glasgow University, to do with medical ethics primarily. I have a degree in philosophy of medical ethics already and I could see myself eventually moving over once I've got enough of a pension built up.

I feel that there have been far too many reorganisations in the Health Service and it's difficult to know whether they are going to help or not. I often feel that the politicians who get involved in primary care without being certain of what they are doing are driven by quick fixes, and the urge to re-write the whole thing in their own image — and we end up with a lot of paperwork. An awful lot of our time is taken up with running a business. In a sense I don't mind that. I'm quite happy to run a small business — that's part of my personality — but it's certainly not what we're trained for.

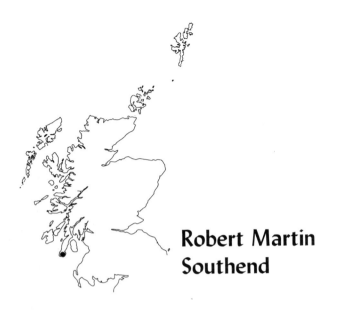

Robert Martin
Southend

When I applied for the job in Southend, I was the youngest by about twenty years – I was twenty-nine – and I've been here for three years now. I'm actually from this area; my family have lived in Campbeltown and Southend for many generations.

I feel that single-handed practice is incredibly important in areas like this. This is an inducement practice, and with only 500 patients we tend to give a much more personal service, and I of course do all my own on call. I spend a long time on call, and in fact that is probably the only down side that I could see to this practice. It would help if we could get mobile phones working here but they don't cover the area very well. At the moment we are lucky that we have an associate GP who works half his time in Southend and the other half in Carradale.

The patients themselves appreciate the personal service; they don't have to make an appointment, they just come along and are seen in turn. We do one surgery a day, Monday to Saturday, but patients can always phone to be seen outside these hours. I appreciate the one-to-one contact I have with my patients, and they like the fact that they see the same doctor who knows them well, plus of course, I'm a dispensing doctor so they don't even have to go to the chemist to get their medication.

We carry out a full range of all the clinics; we've no option here, there's no big hospital. The nearest is in Oban which, from this surgery, is 100 miles away. We have to do everything including casualty, resuscitation and minor surgery; everything that could be done under a local anaesthetic basically. My wife Lorna does all the paperwork, as it is in fact a business as well, and unfortunately there is a lot of paperwork generated. Being a small practice doesn't make the paperwork any less.

We're concerned that they'll move us in with other people, but there is no way that we could be part of another practice. I initially tried cross covering with Campbeltown but with the distance involved it was just ridiculous. I see myself living here until I retire and beyond – I hope that we'll be able to provide a service for many years to come. I think everybody should have equal access to all the services and if people have to travel to Glasgow to get them, then I encourage my patients to do that, but people are afraid. There are some farmers in this area who don't go into Campbeltown; the most they do is come to the village store, so you have a fight on your hands.

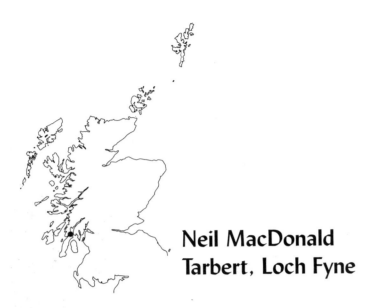

Neil MacDonald
Tarbert, Loch Fyne

I went into single-handed practice because my father was an old-style general practitioner and I wanted to copy him. I came from a little place called Scourie in Sutherland, and, liking the countryside I always thought I'd go into single-handed practice somewhere in the islands. I was in Aviemore for about nine years before coming here twenty-three years ago and I am just about to retire.

Tarbert is a beautiful spot and a great community and the local people are friendly, welcoming and hospitable. This is a big practice with 1800 patients and we have good purpose-built premises which enable me to have a registrar. Registrars, who are doctors in training, have been very stimulating and they also help relieve the workload. In addition, I have an associate GP which is a great boon in relieving the pressure of work. I am beginning to find it very exhausting when I have to get up at night; I was recently up to about 4.00 a.m. on two successive nights and that's beginning to be too much for me. Normally, the way I do things is to have a surgery all morning, Monday to Friday and I work very hard in those four to five hours. I then go home for a

bite to eat and have two to three visits to do in the afternoon. I no longer have afternoon or evening surgeries and the patients accept this. Hospital consultants come from Glasgow and see patients in my surgery with me. This is all very friendly and keeps me in touch with a whole variety of specialties.

I like to spend time in community activities with music being my main interest. I started up the Gaelic choir here and I still have a large part in running it. I have also helped to start up a barbershop chorus; I love harmonising and we've now got fourteen in our chorus. I also enjoy playing bridge but that has fallen by the wayside recently because of lack of numbers. Having been brought up in the Highlands, I like hill walking and still go back to my original home in the northwest where my sister still runs a croft.

I think my family has suffered because I have been a single-handed doctor. I didn't see as much of my children as I would have liked when they were growing up. I was out so much and when I was at home I was bogged down with paperwork. However, I've no regrets and the job satisfaction has been enormous. The essence of general practice is communication and the ability to get on with patients. Without this, you would never survive as a single-handed GP. I don't know what's going to happen in the future; it concerns me to observe the recruitment problems, particularly for isolated areas. All I can say is that it has been a most fulfilling experience for me.

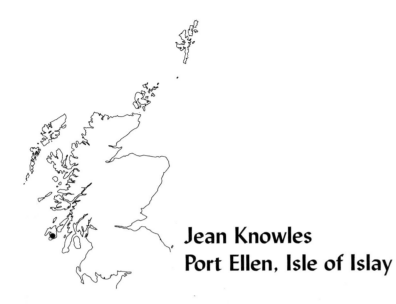

Jean Knowles
Port Ellen, Isle of Islay

I had not planned to work in a single-handed practice on an island. It was probably just chance in that it was a time when jobs were not particularly easy to get and I applied for this post in 1988 and was appointed. There are 1300 patients in the practice which means that I am fully occupied. I enjoy the freedom of being in charge and responsible for all my own actions. You cannot depend on anyone else when you are on your own and it means that you have to be self-reliant. The range of clinical problems is similar to any other practice ranging from the usual childhood ailments to major crises like heart attacks and strokes. I have a fairly clear mental picture of what is happening in the practice at any one time, and I follow things through and do not lose track of patients, as tends to happen in larger group practices.

You get to know people on a completely different level from the way city doctors know their patients. I think this is what makes single-handed practice unique in that you are closer to your patients' lives and can practice family medicine in a way that is just not possible in an urban setting. There is enormous trust between patient and doctor and people will sometimes tell you the most amazing stories about their lives. Knowledge of the community also alerts you to when people are not coping when they claim that they have no problems and everything is all right.

You have to accept that to survive here people are going to know about your social life. Your receptionist has to be your patient and your friend, and your friends who live locally have to be your patients, so everybody accepts the situation. There is no point in worrying about that or shutting yourself off. The fact that you are on call most of the time and have to drive a lot puts some constraints on what you can and cannot do but you just have to get on with it.

I do get frustrated by the hours that I have to work and there are times when I wonder how long I can keep it up. However, these thoughts do not last very long as it becomes a way of life with its own set patterns and routines. I try to get involved as much as I can with community affairs and have served on the local festival committee for ten years which is a pleasant way of making a contribution to the life of the island.

While there may be pressures to reduce the number of single-handed practices, islands like this will always require a doctor. There is more than enough to do and the range of medical care keeps you on your toes. With time, there may be an argument for having two doctors in this practice, but having invested my own money in the practice premises, I am here until I retire.

Iris Ritchie
Drummore

I am quite new to single-handed practice having been here for less than a year. I previously lived and worked in Northern Ireland where I was born. We moved here for a number of reasons, mainly due to the fact that my husband and I were disillusioned with the political situation in Northern Ireland and we thought that we would like to bring up our children in an environment outwith the divisions which make life so difficult there. I had previously been a trainee in Stranraer some ten years ago, so the area was not totally unknown to me. It has been a huge decision for us to come here as we have had to leave our home, family and everyone we knew, yet it was an easy decision as we felt it was right for us.

Drummore is at the south west tip of Scotland and there are 800 patients in a dispensing practice. The patients have been very welcoming and probably enjoy having a regular GP again as my predecessor had been off ill for some time and the practice had been covered by a succession of locums. I run a mixture of open surgeries and appointments which mean that the patients have the best of both worlds. They can be seen in the mornings for acute problems while specific complaints or follow ups can be dealt with in the afternoons. Being single-handed means that you really get to know your patients and the continuity of care provided is very satisfying, not only for me but for the patients as well. I feel much more in touch with patients than previously when I was in a busy group practice in an urban area.

I am not completely isolated here in that I share night-call duties with the GPs in Stranraer, which means that I can actually get time off. The other GPs in the area are also very friendly and I can always contact them for advice. With young children there is not much time for a social life outwith family activities but I have already made some good friends here. Having children is a way of meeting people through playgroups and young women's groups and this keeps me in contact with the life of the community.

Being single-handed here is not as stressful as it might be, as I have good arrangements for time off and night calls. It is the doctors in more remote areas who are stuck by the phone twenty-four hours a day who must find it extremely stressful. It is practices like that that will be increasingly difficult to sustain as young doctors are no longer willing to make these sacrifices. If doctors were assured of regular time off, then many more might actually opt to be single-handed where you are free to make your own decisions and have a true sense of ownership of your practice.

The South
Ecclefechan
Lauder

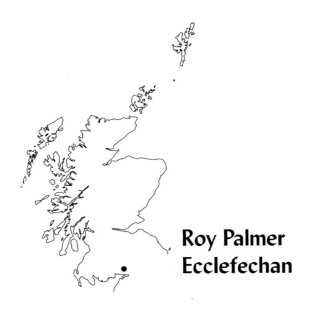

Roy Palmer
Ecclefechan

I was originally in a group practice near Bristol, but after a dispute I thought that single-handed practice would be the answer for me. I wanted to be my own boss and do things my own way and in my own time. Ecclefechan is nicely situated ten miles north of the border with England, not far from the motorway, in soft rolling countryside, and with two hospitals within twenty miles. When I arrived, the practice had become run down and disorganised with no proper premises, and we had to create a new purpose-built surgery.

I like the country rather than large towns because you can get to know your patients better and be part of a community. This practice is a dispensing practice and we have a health visitor and a district nurse with a clinical psychologist who comes once a week. My wife has been my practice manager for the last fifteen years and she is always there to organise me, acts as one of the dispensers and ensures that I don't forget things. Without her I would never be able to do this job. Over the years, I've built extensions to the surgery which provide rooms for the nurses and the treatment room for dressings and minor surgical procedures. There is also a health promotion room which has exercise equipment for rehabilitation and keep-fit programmes.

I get involved quite a lot in the community and have helped in fundraising, which has resulted in a new park with a pavilion, football pitch, picnic area, putting green and nature trail. Last year the village received a prize in the Scotland in Bloom competition – we're all very proud of that. I'm also very keen on racing and am medical officer at Carlisle Race Course. I'm keen on supporting the local trainers and I really enjoy the whole racing scene.

As far as the future of single-handed practice is concerned, I think it's very important to retain this aspect of medical practice. The development of the Associate Practitioner Scheme has certainly helped doctors in remote parts of the country. In this area we have formed a co-operative, which means that my night work is now shared with a larger number of doctors which means I have much more time off. In the past, I shared a rota with a local practice which meant that I was on call one night in three and every third weekend.

One of my sons is a medical student and I'd be thrilled if he succeeded me in the practice and allowed me to wind down a bit. However, that is for the future. For the present, I thoroughly enjoy the variety of work and have been more than fulfilled as a single-handed doctor.

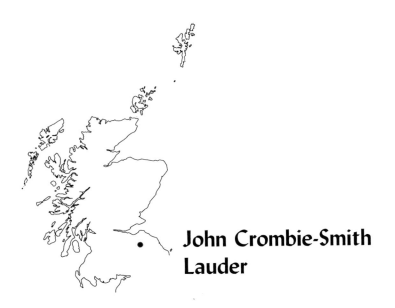

John Crombie-Smith
Lauder

My father was a general practitioner in the village of Lauder where I now work. When he was getting up to retirement age I made the suggestion that perhaps it would be nice for us to work together. That worked fairly well for two to three years until he got to seventy-odd and was obliged to retire. At that point I had the idea of merging this single-handed practice with the one in Stow. As time went on I felt that I was losing control, that other people were making decisions and that I had no part in them. Consequently I decided that I would in fact like to have a go at operating the practice on my own. There was a co-operative being started for night and weekend work; this meant that I at least had some cover for nights or weekends off. The practice at the moment is only about 1100 patients, but the population is still growing. I find that living in the community however, the co-op being at least twenty minutes away by car, I'd feel guilty about leaving my patients untended. Many nights and weekends I find that I see more of my own patients than the co-op does, but at least they know that if I am not there then there is a back-up service that will provide for them.

I seem to get the idea that more and more people look upon general practice as a job and not as a vocation. I think the whole concept of general practice is one of service, so it is a bit like being a monk in the middle ages, but the concept, in my mind, is that you are part of a community and the idea is to provide a service to that community, to be there for the people when they are in trouble. It may be an old fashioned idea but I still think that's the essence of medicine as a whole. I suppose I am getting cynical in my old age – I can foresee the Health Board cutting the number of GPs in the Borders from about seventy to about twelve with the other services being provided by nursing staff, paramedics and pharmacists purely for cost-effectiveness.

I do quite a bit of horse trial support work. I am a member of the Medical Equestrian Association and I go and stand around at horse trials while other idiots run around on horses and fall off and I pick up the broken bones. I am not a keen gardener; I get somebody else to do that for me. On Saturday afternoon and Sunday I probably sit and put my feet up more often than not, read a magazine, catch up on the news or watch Star Trek.